CHUCKIE AND PUNKIN RULE THE WORLD

WRITTEN BY: DR. SYDNEY ROSS-DAVIS

ILLUSTRATED BY: DR. ALICIA CHRISTY

MOLO GLOBAL
PUBLISHING

ISBN Paperback: 978-1955512-93-0
ISBN E-book: 978-1-955512-96-1
Library of Congress Control Number: 2021925743

Published in Silver Spring, Maryland by Molo Global Publishing, an imprint of Molo Global Consulting, LLC.

This book is dedicated to Punkin Wunkin and Chuckie Charles, our children, and inspiration for this book. Parenting is the toughest job you will ever love. We look forward to chronicling the adventures of our grandchildren, too.

Chuckie Charles and Punkin Wunkin were always big and small.

Punkin is the short one, and Chuckie is quite tall.

Punkin Wunkin and Chuckie Charles are the very best of friends.

They sing, they dance, they laugh, and they run as fast as wind!

Chuckie's laugh is a giggle.
Punkin's laugh is a snort

Chuckie likes to play music.

Punkin likes to play sports.

Chuckie has to duck under tables. Punkin can walk straight through

Chuckie's blanky is red.
Punkin's blanky is blue

Punkin speaks with a whisper.

Chuckie calls out with a shout.

Punkin's hair falls in braids.

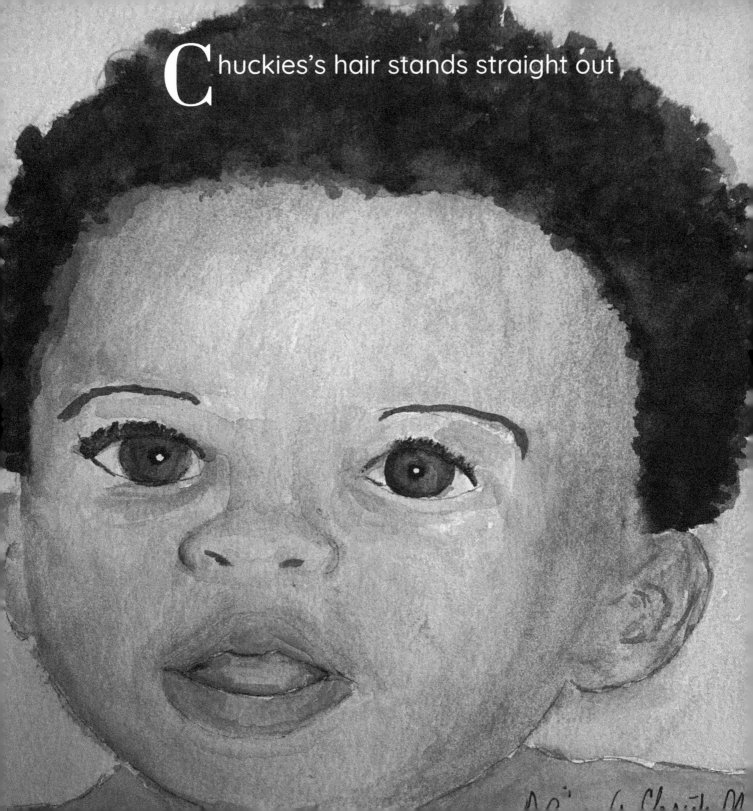

Chuckies's hair stands straight out

Punkin's mommy works at a desk.

Chuckie's mom works at a Fort.

Chuckie's daddy is quite tall.
Punkin's daddy is quite short.

Chuckies's daddy goes to work at a lab.

Punkin's daddy goes to work at a court.

Short or tall, giggle or snort, lab or court, desk or fort, music or sports. They talk, they laugh, they run, they play, and Punkin and Chuckie have a really great day!

The End

ABOUT THE AUTHOR/ILLUSTRATOR

WE ARE LIFELONG FRIENDS juggling roles as parents, partners and physicians. We feel privileged to share the stories of our children's adventures and misadventures! Come celebrate with us!

CPSIA information can be obtained
at www.ICGtesting.com
Printed in the USA
LVHW072035020222
710072LV00008B/332